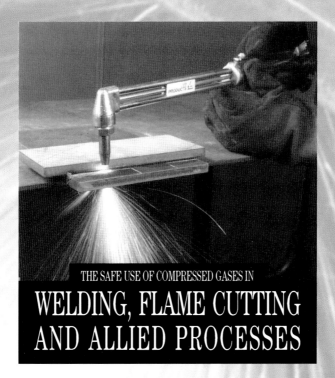

THE SAFE USE OF COMPRESSED GASES IN

WELDING, FLAME CUTTING AND ALLIED PROCESSES

HSE BOOKS

*Acknowledgement: HSE gratefully
acknowledges the help given by Air Products
Plc in illustrating this booklet.*

CONTENTS

PREFACE

The main aim of this publication is to promote safer use of compressed gases in gas welding, flame cutting and related processes. The intention is to protect people at work and others who may be affected by the work activity, and to reduce the injuries and damage caused by fires and explosions. Although it is not aimed at small firms, it will be useful to managers, safety specialists, manufacturers, suppliers and installers of equipment, and others who have duties concerned with selecting, using and maintaining the equipment.

The publication is intended to:

- increase awareness of the potential hazards involved and the precautions to be taken;
- give guidance on appropriate British, European and international standards for equipment;
- advise on safe operating procedures;
- advise on the need for training, personal protective equipment, fire precautions, maintenance, examination and testing of the equipment.

Where references to British or other standards are made in this publication, other appropriate standards (eg CEN standards) which are not specifically referred to but which are current, or are subsequently developed, may be equally acceptable alternatives. References in the text are given in abbreviated form; full references are to be found in the reference section at the end of the publication.

INTRODUCTION

1   This publication gives technical guidance on the safe use of compressed gases and equipment in gas welding and allied processes such as brazing, flame cutting (often referred to as 'burning'), descaling, flame cleaning and gouging. It covers:

- design, construction and provision of equipment;
- handling and storage of gas cylinders;
- personal protective equipment;
- operating procedures;
- fire precautions;
- examination and testing of equipment;
- special hazards and precautions in the use of fuel gases and oxygen.

2   It also provides information on hazards and risks and the protective measures needed to control them. (Employers are legally[1] required to assess the risks in the workplace and take all reasonably practicable precautions to ensure the safety of workers and members of the public.)

3   It does not include guidance on:

- hazards and precautions when welding or flame cutting anything that may contain flammable materials or residues - advice on this is given in HSE booklet HS(G)5[2] ;
- use of acetylene at pressures above 0.62 bar (9 psi);
- hazards in using oxygen for thermic lancing and flame spraying equipment;
- all forms of electric welding equipment and plasma processes where compressed gas is used for shielding purposes;
- hazards from toxic fumes - advice is available in Guidance Note EH 54[3] (assessment of exposure to welding fumes) and Guidance Note EH 55[4] (control of exposure to welding fumes);
- use of gas welding and cutting equipment in mines.

Processes

4   In principle, all the processes described in this publication operate in the same way: a fuel gas is mixed with oxygen or air in a

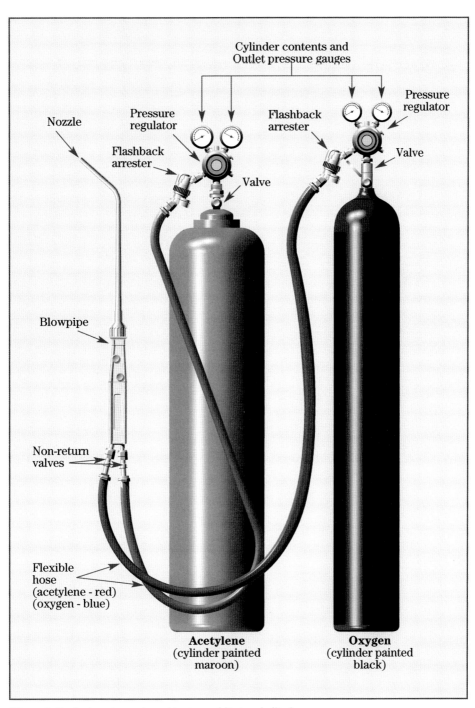

Figure 1 Typical equipment used in gas welding and allied processes

blowpipe (often referred to as a 'torch') to produce a flame that is hot enough for the process. In flame cutting, the flame heats the workpiece to a temperature at which the metal oxide can be formed from an additional supply of oxygen at the blowpipe. The oxide is melted and blown away by the force of the flame.

Equipment

5   Typical components of the equipment used in gas welding and allied processes are:

- a gas supply installation - cylinders or in bulk;
- a means of isolating the gas supply;
- a pressure regulator fitted to the outlet valve of the gas cylinder or the gas supply outlet point - used to reduce and control gas pressure;
- fixed pipework and/or flexible hose to distribute the gases;
- a burner device where the fuel gas is mixed with air or oxygen and ignited;
- safety devices to limit over-pressure and prevent flashbacks and return flow;
- ancillary equipment, eg flow meters (to aid process control) and flux dispensers for brazing.

FIRE, EXPLOSION AND OTHER HAZARDS

Hazards

6   The main hazards addressed in this publication are:

- fires and explosions resulting from the release of flammable gases to the atmosphere from leaks at joints, hose connections or fittings - the leaks may be into open workshop conditions or they may accumulate in confined or semi-confined spaces;
- enhanced fires and explosions from release of oxygen to the atmosphere and accumulation of an oxygen-enriched atmosphere in clothing or in confined spaces;
- fires and explosions inside the equipment caused by a flashback from the blowpipe - this occurs when a flammable mixture of fuel gas and air or oxygen is present upstream because gas lines were not completely purged before lighting up or because fuel gas has back-fed into the oxygen/air supply (or vice versa). Possible causes of back-feeding are excessive pressure differentials in the gas lines, a leaking control valve, or gas supply interruption after a hose has been trapped or kinked or the blowpipe nozzle has become blocked;
- fires and explosions inside the equipment or cylinders caused by decomposition or detonation of acetylene in the absence of air or oxygen - caused by, for example, flashback at the blowpipe or overheating of a cylinder;
- fires and explosions inside the equipment when high-pressure oxygen (without fuel gas) promotes the combustion of materials such as oil, grease, organic compounds (solids or powders), metals like aluminium and their alloys, and the elastomers used in valve seats and seals;
- burns from the blowpipe flame, hot slag or hot surfaces (even after the flame has been extinguished) either by direct contact with bare skin or by setting clothing on fire;
- eye injuries from hot particles (eg slag, molten metal and cutting sparks), heat, intense light and ultra-violet radiation;
- fires when combustible or flammable materials left near the process area or touching the workpiece catch light;
- explosion from over-pressurisation of the equipment;
- personal injuries caused by, for example, accidents when handling cylinders.

Acetylene

7   Commercial acetylene usually has a garlic-like odour, and is slightly lighter than air. It is supplied as a gas dissolved under pressure in a solvent, usually acetone, and is contained in a porous mass inside its cylinder. It has a lower flammable limit of 2.5% by volume in air but no clearly defined upper limit. Unlike the other fuel gases used in gas welding it is potentially unstable; in either the liquid state or as a gas under pressure it may decompose violently in the absence of oxygen or air. Guidance on acetylene is given in the HSE leaflet *Take care with acetylene*.[5]

8   There are legal controls[6] to ensure the safe manufacture, compression and use of acetylene. Of particular relevance to this guidance is that acetylene pressure must not exceed 0.62 bar (9 psi) unless equipment has been designed to meet HSE Exemption Certificate No2[7] and British Compressed Gases Association Code of Practice CP6 *The safe distribution of acetylene in the pressure range 0-1.5 bar (0-22ibf/in²)*.[8]

Other fuel gases

9   Other than acetylene, the most commonly used fuel gas in gas welding is propane (commonly referred to as 'LPG', or 'liquefied petroleum gas'). Commercial propane may contain considerable amounts of propylene and other hydrocarbons such as butane. It is a colourless gas with a stenching agent added. It is considerably heavier than air, with a relative density of 1.55 at 20°C (air = 1). Its vapour pressure is 8.53 bar absolute at 21.1°C and it is supplied as a liquefied gas in cylinders.

10   Other fuel gases include methylacetylene-propadiene mixtures (which have similar properties to LPG), hydrogen and natural gas.

Oxygen

11   Oxygen is a colourless, normally odourless and non-flammable gas. It is slightly heavier than air. Air normally contains about 21% by volume of oxygen and the manner in which common materials burn in air is well known, but in oxygen concentrations above 21% or at pressures above atmospheric, combustion is more

hazardous. Materials are more easily ignited, they burn faster, they generate higher temperatures and they may be difficult or almost impossible to put out. Materials such as clothing, plastics and metals which do not normally burn in air may burn vigorously in an atmosphere rich in oxygen. Oil or grease may react explosively with pressurised oxygen. A room atmosphere with more than about 25% of oxygen by volume can be dangerous, particularly if it is a confined space, and fatal accidents have occurred. Even in the open air, oxygen may remain trapped in clothing or hair, which can then easily be ignited, causing serious or fatal burn injuries.

Precautions to prevent fires and explosions

12   The main precautions to minimise risk of fires or explosions are to:

●   provide the appropriate equipment and installations and check they have been designed and constructed to recognised standards (paragraphs 14-52);

●   ensure cylinder storage and bulk supply facilities are safe (paragraphs 53-65);

●   route, position and mark fixed gas supply pipework in a safe manner (paragraphs 25-28);

●   ensure safe cylinder handling techniques are practised (paragraphs 66-68);

●   ensure operatives use suitable personal protective equipment (paragraphs 69-71);

●   provide appropriate training, instruction and supervision to ensure correct operating procedures are followed (paragraphs 72-74);

●   ensure adequate precautions when working in confined spaces (paragraphs 88-90);

●   take appropriate fire precautions (paragraphs 93-95);

●   follow adequate procedures for regular examination, testing and maintenance of equipment (paragraphs 96-100).

13   These precautions are explained more fully in the rest of this publication.

DESIGN, CONSTRUCTION AND PROVISION OF EQUIPMENT

14 Regulation 4 of the Provision and Use of Work Equipment Regulations 1998[9] requires that every employer shall ensure that work equipment is so constructed or adapted as to be suitable for the purpose for which it is used or provided. Regulation 12 requires that employers take measures to prevent or control exposure to risk from certain specified hazards. In the context of this publication, it is important that gas welding equipment is constructed from materials selected to be compatible with the gases that are used. A general standard specification for materials is given in British Standard BS EN 29539[10], which is referred to in other European standards. It includes special requirements for oxygen and acetylene service.

15 There is a general requirement for the equipment to be gas tight to minimise leakage to the atmosphere. Requirements are specified in British Standard BS EN 29090[11] which is referred to in the relevant European standards for gas welding and similar equipment.

Oxygen service

16 Before specifying materials for oxygen service, specialist knowledge is required of the properties of the materials concerned, service requirements and relevant test methods. In principle:

- copper and copper alloys such as brass and bronze are generally suitable for oxygen service;
- ferrous materials such as mild or stainless steel are widely used, but are generally limited to specific applications where gas velocity does not exceed 15 m/s at 20 bar g;
- light metals such as aluminium and its alloys are generally unsuitable for use in contact with high-pressure oxygen;
- organic materials used for diaphragms, valve seats, seals, and other similar components need to be chosen from those which are known to be relatively resistant to ignition in oxygen (eg materials based on fluorinated derivatives such as polytetrafluoroethylene (PTFE)).

17 Some relevant guidance may be found in British Standard BS 4N 100[12] which covers design requirements for aircraft oxygen systems and equipment. Guidance has also been published by the American Society for Testing and Materials, in ASTM G 94-88 and ASTM G 63-83a.[13]

18 Where it is essential to use lubricants in equipment for oxygen service, it is important only to use ones that have been shown by appropriate testing to be compatible with oxygen under the service conditions. Lubricants based on hydrocarbons are highly dangerous in oxygen service; a silicone grease has been implicated in at least one incident. Fluorinated compositions have been found to be suitable, but it is advisable to seek the advice of specialist suppliers on the choice of a lubricant.

19 To minimise the risk of fires and explosions, all equipment for oxygen service, particularly for use with compressed oxygen, should be free from any traces of oil, grease, swarf, metal particles, rust, dust, fragments of organic materials (eg those used for seals and gaskets), sealing tape and jointing compounds. The requirement is that equipment is free of any solid or liquid inorganic or organic contaminant. New equipment for oxygen service is usually subjected to rigorous cleaning by the manufacturer to meet the requirements of relevant standards - and may be supplied in sealed bags with documentation indicating that it is suitable for oxygen service. All reasonable precautions should then be taken to ensure that it is not contaminated in storage, use or maintenance. Special attention is needed to ensure the cleanliness of storage and maintenance areas. The protective packaging should be retained unbroken until immediately before the equipment is brought into service.

Acetylene service

20 When acetylene comes into contact with some metals - notably copper, silver and mercury - acetylides may be formed, particularly when moisture is present. Acetylides are unstable and may explode or initiate decomposition of the acetylene. For this reason, copper and alloys containing more than 70% by mass of copper, and silver and alloys with more than 46% of silver are not used either in equipment construction (with the exception of copper for blowpipe nozzles and necks) or in brazing alloys. Neither are light metals such as aluminium, magnesium and zinc normally used in acetylene service, since they may be corroded by impurities in the acetylene. Acetylene supplies normally contain acetone or more rarely dimethyl formamide as solvents for the gas, and it is important that equipment is compatible with these solvents too.

21   Relevant equipment standards take into account the special requirements of acetylene service.

Gas supplies

22   Gas for welding and cutting may be supplied in:

- single transportable gas receptacles, vessels or containers (more commonly known as 'gas cylinders' or 'gas bottles') which may be portable, mobile or connected to fixed pipework;
- two or more cylinders connected together by manifold pipework and possibly mounted in a frame (a 'manifolded cylinder pallet') - multiple arrangements of manifolded cylinders are often referred to as 'banks' or 'bottle banks';
- other piped gas supplies such as bulk supply installations.

Cylinders

23   The gas cylinders are usually seamless or welded steel. New cylinders must comply with the design standards, approval and certification requirements in the Carriage of Dangerous Goods (Classification, Packaging and Labelling) and Use of Transportable Gas Receptacles Regulations 1996 (as amended)[14]. HSE has approved design standards[15] under these Regulations. Most cylinders coming within the scope of this publication comply with these standards although some old cylinders still remain in use which comply with earlier standards. General advice on gas cylinders is given in *The safe use of gas cylinders*[16].

Acetylene cylinders

24   Acetylene cylinders are filled with a porous mass and normally contain a solvent, usually acetone, to stabilise

Figure 2 Gas cylinders

the gas. Acetylene generators, producing acetylene from calcium carbide and water for direct use in welding, etc are no longer in common use and are not covered by this publication.

High-pressure manifolds and distribution systems

25   The Pressure Systems Safety Regulations 2000[17] apply to the pipework connected to gas cylinders. When cylinders are connected together by a manifold operating at full cylinder-charging pressure, it is important to ensure that the manifold and all associated pipework is capable of withstanding the maximum pressures likely to be encountered in the system.

26   Additional safety equipment or features to be considered in the design of high-pressure manifolds and distribution pipework include:

- pressure regulator to control gas supply pressure to downstream equipment;
- flame arrester to prevent propagation of flashbacks from downstream equipment;
- non-return valves to prevent oxygen back-feeding into fuel pipelines and vice versa;
- pressure gauge to monitor pressure;
- isolation valve for rapid isolation of the gas supply in an emergency;
- pressure-relief device to prevent over-pressurisation of downstream equipment;
- vent and purge connections so that purging routines can ensure that flammable gas - air mixtures are not supplied to downstream equipment;
- flow meters to aid process control.

27   Further guidance on the provision of safety devices is available in the British Compressed Gases Association's (BCGA) Code of Practice CP 4[18].

28   Special conditions apply to acetylene manifolds and distribution systems depending on the operating pressure. Manifolds, valves and fittings must be capable of withstanding the thermal and mechanical stresses resulting from acetylene decomposition. Guidance can be found in BCGA's Code of Practice

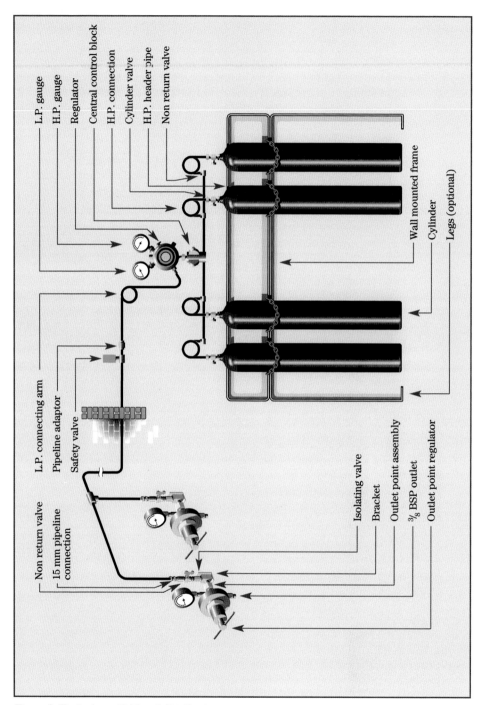

Figure 3 Typical manifold and distribution system

CP 5[19] (for acetylene at full cylinder pressure) which recommends the use of carbon steel for manifolds and pipework, and CP 6[8] (for acetylcnc up to 1.5 bar **g**).

Bulk gas supplies

29   Where the rate of gas consumption is sufficiently high, economic factors may justify the use of bulk gas supplies.

●   Oxygen supplies in large engineering works or shipbuilding/repair yards may consist of a bulk cryogenic liquid oxygen storage installation and vaporiser to produce gas for the distribution system. It is recommended that these installations comply with BCGA's Code of Practice CP 19[20]. It is also recommended that oxygen supplies are odorised if a risk assessment identifies that oxygen enrichment in confined spaces is a potential hazard. Odorisation is intended to provide a warning in the event of oxygen leakage (as it does with natural gas and LPG). It is common practice in shipbuilding/repairing where confined-space working is often necessary. HSE Guidance Note CS 7[21] gives guidance on odorisation of oxygen supplies in shipyards, and its principles have application generally wherever odorisation is used.

●   Guidance on bulk storage of LPGA is given in Code of Practice 1[22] and HSE's CHIS4.

●   Acetylene is only supplied in bulk by means of manifolded cylinders mounted in a frame for ease of transportation.

●   Bulk hydrogen is not normally needed for welding, but the gas may be transported in bulk as compressed gas in large cylinders mounted on road vehicles known as 'tube trailers'. Fixed installations of manifolded cylinders are charged from the tube trailers.

Figure 4 Bulk supply storage - liquid oxygen

Pressure regulators and pressure gauges

Regulators

30　Pressure regulators are intended to control gas pressure from supply pressure (cylinder, bulk or manifolded supplies) to operating pressure. They are not intended as protective devices to prevent over-pressurisation of downstream equipment. For supply pressures up to 200 bar g, it is recommended that regulators are used that comply with British Standards BS EN 585[23] or BS EN ISO 2503[24], or BS 3016[25] for LPG. For supply pressures in the range 200-300 bar g, BS EN ISO 2503[24] is the relevant standard to use. It is important to ensure that the regulator in use can safely handle the maximum supply pressure, since it is possible to connect a regulator designed for 200 bar g maximum inlet pressure to the valve on a 300 bar g cylinder. This mis-match is unlikely to result in immediate mechanical failure but, with an oxygen regulator, the internal components may not be suitable for use at the higher pressure.

31　One of the safety features of the standards for regulators is pressure shock type-testing for oxygen regulators. It tests for resistance to the internal ignition which could arise, for example, when the cylinder or manifold valve is opened for the first time after the regulator is connected to a fresh oxygen gas supply. Adiabatic compression may cause localised heating. The result could be a metal-oxygen fire with risk of burn injuries from fire, explosion and eruption of molten metal. Another safety feature required by the standards ensures that high pressure gas is either safely retained or vented when the low pressure side of a regulator is exposed to gas at full cylinder charging pressure if its outlet is deliberately closed. Fortunately, there are few recorded incidents of failure of pressure regulators in which gas at cylinder charging pressure

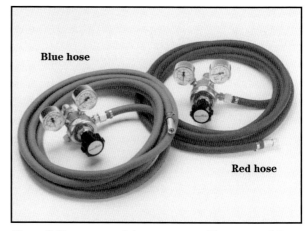

Blue hose

Red hose

Figure 5　Pressure regulators, gauges and hose assemblies

has been released to the atmosphere or to downstream equipment. Those that have occurred have been the result of deterioration of the first stage valve or rupture of the diaphragm.

32   For pressure regulators for manifolded gas supplies BS EN ISO 7291[26] applies. Pressure regulators designed for cylinders are commonly used for manifold applications, and may be acceptable where gas flow rates are limited, providing they comply with the standards referred to in paragraph 30. For large systems with high gas flow, regulators which comply with the ISO (or CEN equivalent) standard are recommended.

Gauges

33   Pressure readings are useful to a gas welder in order to control the process and check the availability of gas supply; pressure gauges may be fitted for these purposes to cylinders and to distribution pipework and manifold supply installations. Gauges are often fitted to pressure regulators - on the upstream side to give an indication of cylinder supply pressure (a 'contents' gauge), and on the low pressure side to indicate outlet pressure. Some adjustable regulators have no provision for gauges but have an indication of outlet pressure marked on the regulator housing, and some deliver gas at a fixed outlet pressure (eg for LPG).

34   Pressure gauges complying with British Standard BS EN 562[27], ISO 5171[28] are preferred. Alternatively, gauges complying with BS EN 837[29] may be acceptable. These standards incorporate safety features including safe venting if the Bourdon tube fails and releases gas.

Hoses, hose connections and hose assemblies

Hoses

35   Rubber hose complying with British Standard BS EN 559[30], ISO 3821[31] or equivalent is recommended for use in gas welding and cutting processes, which are often carried out in aggressive working environments. Hoses satisfying these standards are reinforced with an outer protective cover designed to be resistant to hot surfaces, molten slag or sparks, and made with linings that resist the action of hydrocarbons (for LPG hose), acetone or dimethyl formamide (for acetylene hose), and ignition in an atmosphere of oxygen (for all services). Burst pressure is 60 bar g and maximum working pressure 20 bar g. The colour coding for this type of hose is:

- red for acetylene and other fuel gases except LPG;
- orange for LPG;
- blue for oxygen (although green may be found in equipment supplied from the USA);
- black for non-combustible gases (eg compressed air).

36   Hose meeting the requirements of BS 3212[32] is recommended for LPG vapour-phase applications other than welding or cutting.

37   Hose made of thermoplastics materials is not generally suitable for welding and cutting, because it does not have the same resistance to hot surfaces or hot particles as reinforced rubber hose. However, there may be no practicable alternative to its use for the small diameter hose (less than 5 mm) used with the small blowpipes needed in jewellery work, dental laboratories, etc. Hose this small may not be available in reinforced rubber. BS EN 1327[33] is the standard for thermoplastics hose.

38   Hose is also used in manifold systems at cylinder supply pressures and for cylinder filling operations. A relevant Standard is BS EN 14114[34].

Connections

39   It is recommended that hose connections (comprising hose nipples and 'bull-nose' hose connections) comply with British Standard BS EN 560[35], ISO 3253[36] or equivalent. Thread sizes specified in these standards are based on Whitworth dimensions, which are generally used in this field in many countries. Right-hand threads are used for oxygen and non-combustible gases; left-hand threads are used for fuel gases, with the hexagon nuts on their union connections notched to aid identification.

40   Hose connections may also be made with a quick-action coupling - a male probe fitted to the end of the hose and a female connector with a self-sealing valve usually fitted to a fixed piece of equipment or gas supply outlet point. The probe is pushed into the

female fitting where it locks in position and automatically opens the internal valve. Connections of this type are simple and quick to operate and there is no need to use a spanner to tighten any nuts. Problems are that the male probe may become damaged (eg from being dragged along the ground or over-use) and cause the coupling to leak, and there is a possibility of connecting the hose to the wrong gas outlet. Both should be avoided if couplings comply with British Standard BS EN 561[37] or with ISO 7289[38]. These require hard materials of construction to be used for the probes, and their design dimensions are intended to prevent interchangeability between oxygen and fuel gas connections.

Hose assemblies

41   Hose lengths are usually supplied in the UK as pre-assembled units complete with connection fittings crimped to the ends of the hose. Hose and hose nipple dimensions are matched by the supplier to ensure a good fit. The recommended standard for hose assemblies is BS EN 1256[39], which specifies requirements for leak tightness and resistance to axial loading. Worm drive or similar clips are not recommended for fastening hoses.

Blowpipes

42   Welding, cutting and heating blowpipes (or torches) are designed to burn fuel gas with oxygen or air in such a way that a flame is produced safely under controlled conditions. The essential components are gas inlet connections, a handle (or shank), control valves, pipeways, mixing chamber and a nozzle. An extra gas pipeway (or 'channel') is necessary in a cutting blowpipe for the cutting oxygen. Some glassworking blowpipes retain the separate gas pipeways for fuel gas and oxygen through the nozzle, so that gas mixing takes place on the outside surface of the nozzle, eliminating the need for a mixing chamber. Some blowpipes, commonly those used with LPG in plumbing and roofing work, are 'air-aspirated'; air from the atmosphere mixes with the fuel gas at the nozzle or just upstream of it.

43   To enable the operator to work safely, a blowpipe needs to satisfy several requirements. It needs to be:

●   suitable for the gases in use and for the temperature, pressure and gas flow of the process;

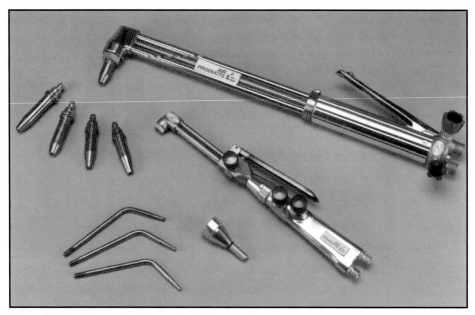

Figure 6 Blowpipes and cutting and welding nozzles

- capable of producing a flame that is stable and adjustable to the demands of the work;
- resistant to intermittent or sustained backfire (in which the flame returns from the nozzle into the mixing chamber).

44 These, and other safety-related issues are addressed by British Standard BS EN 5172[40] which covers hand-held blowpipes for gas welding, cutting and heating processes. Blowpipes complying with this standard or equivalent are recommended for use where applicable. Other standards are relevant to the air-aspirated blowpipes used with LPG:

- BS EN 731[41] or equivalent for LPG at a controlled pressure supplied from cylinders fitted with pressure regulators;
- BS EN 521[42] or equivalent for LPG at the uncontrolled vapour pressure of the gas;
- there is no relevant British, European or international standard for blowpipes designed for use with LPG in the liquid phase - they tend to be specialised devices and the advice of the manufacturer should be sought.

Safety devices

45   Appropriate safety devices are recommended to reduce the risk of fires and explosions in equipment and hoses which, if unchecked, may cause fires at gas cylinder connections and possibly gas cylinder explosions. For oxy-fuel gas equipment, use of safety devices complying with the requirements of BS EN 730[43], ISO 5175[44] or equivalent standards is recommended. Further guidance on the provision of safety devices (and other more general matters) is given in BCGA's Code of Practice CP 7[45].

Non-return valves

46   It is strongly recommended that non-return valves are provided at each blowpipe inlet connection to reduce the risk of oxygen reverse flow into the fuel gas line and vice versa. They offer no specific protection against flashbacks, but they should reduce the risk of them occurring by preventing the formation of flammable mixtures.

47   Obsolete designs of non-return valves sometimes referred to as 'hose check valves' or 'hose protectors' which rely on a floating plate to stop reverse flow are ineffective at low flow rates. They do not comply with the above standards; their removal from service is recommended, followed immediately by replacement with valves that do comply. In dental and jewellery work, the weight of non-return valves may interfere with the handling of the very small blowpipes used, and they may be located in the hose near the blowpipe to overcome this. Non-return valves are not necessary with the external-surface-mixing blowpipes used in glassworking or with air-aspirated blowpipes. With these designs, it is inconceivable that reverse flow could occur.

Flame arresters

48   Flame arresters incorporating pressure or temperature actuated cut-off valves - sometimes known as 'flashback arresters' - reduce the risk of flashbacks entering cylinders or distribution pipework, and help protect cylinders from the effects of fire by cutting off the gas supply in the event of a flashback. They should be fitted at the pressure regulator outlet connection of all acetylene cylinders or outlet points from acetylene distribution systems and manifolds. It is highly advisable to fit flame arresters incorporating cut-off valves at the outlet connections of pressure regulators for other fuel gases and oxygen as well. They are particularly valuable where flashbacks are more likely to occur (eg in training establishments or where there is multiple usage from a manifold system) or where immediate access to the gas supply control valves may be difficult in an emergency - because of the lengths of hoses in use or because of work on different levels or in confined spaces. An alternative location for the flame arrester is the blowpipe inlet connections, but although in this location they offer worthwhile protection against flashbacks originating in the blowpipe, they offer no fire protection from a sustained hose fire, eg from a hose leak ignited by a blowpipe or hot surface. Flame arresters are not necessary with air aspirated blowpipes.

Pressure relief valves

49   It is not normally considered necessary to incorporate pressure relief valves into equipment located downstream of pressure regulators with maximum outlet pressures of 20 bar g or less. In the kind of welding and cutting operations covered by this publication, the maximum outlet pressure of pressure regulators normally lies in the range 1.5-20 bar g and, providing these pressures are not exceeded, over-pressurisation of downstream equipment will not occur. The design pressure of industrial grade welding hose meeting BS EN 559[30] is 20 bar g, for example, and normally this will only be exceeded if the pressure regulator fails and gas at uncontrolled supply pressure passes downstream. This, fortunately, is a rare event! The outlet chamber of any pressure regulator is required to withstand full cylinder pressure or vent gas safely in accordance with the relevant standards, but welding hose may burst if subjected to a pressure of 60 bar g. This could happen with oxygen or hydrogen, but not with acetylene, LPG, methylacetylene-propadiene mixtures or with natural gas from low-pressure piped gas supplies, since none of these gases is supplied at pressures exceeding 60 bar g.

Figure 7 Flame (flashback) arresters

Welding flux dispensers

50   Welding flux dispensers are designed to provide a continuous supply of flux to the fuel gas stream in brazing operations. Usually, a container is filled with a liquid flux solution, and flux vapours are entrained in the gas supply by passing the gas through the container. The flux is usually a solution of methyl borate in methanol, acetone or other organic solvent. The main hazards associated with welding flux dispensers are:

● fire hazard from handling flammable liquid (the flux solution) and possibly spilling it during filling;
● flashback into the dispenser, possibly causing it to rupture and violently eject burning liquid;
● over-pressurisation of the dispenser causing flammable liquid to be ejected.

51   There is no recognised standard for flux dispensers. To reduce the risk of accidents in their use, adequate precautions are needed in the handling and storage of the flammable flux, and general advice on storage of flammable liquids in containers is given in HSE's guidance booklet HS(G)51[46]. It is important that the dispenser is fitted with a flame arrester, located downstream between the dispenser and the blowpipe. Flow rates need to be carefully controlled though, to ensure that the flame arrester does not become blocked with flux residues. The risk of over-pressurisation should be avoided if the design pressure of the dispenser is greater than the rated maximum outlet pressure of the pressure regulator which controls the gas supply to it.

Small welding kits

52   Pre-assembled small welding kits usually consist of gas supplies in disposable or refillable containers, gas supply controls, pressure regulators, hoses connected to a blowpipe and appropriate safety devices. The kit, usually mounted in a carrying frame or structure, may be used in industry as well as at home. Design and construction of these kits, including the carrying structure, is specified by British Standard BS 6942[47] Part 1 and BS EN 1326[47]. If the kit includes a container of flammable liquid to modify the burning characteristics of the gases, similar precautions should be considered, as appropriate, to those described in paragraph 51 for welding flux dispensers.

STORAGE AND HANDLING OF GAS CYLINDERS

Storage hazards

53   The principal hazards associated with the storage of gas cylinders include:

- cylinders becoming over-pressurised and exploding if they are exposed to heat or engulfed in a building fire;
- explosion, which may be accompanied by the sudden release of fuel gas or oxygen causing an immediate and dramatic increase in fire size;
- decomposition of acetylene, initiated by exposure to heat and which may result in exploding cylinders;
- ignited releases of acetylene from operation of bursting discs or fusible plugs;
- ignited releases of LPG from pressure relief valves, resulting in jet flames and subsequent escalation of the fire;
- leakage of gas from cylinder valves;
- tampering by unauthorised people;
- vandalism.

54   These hazards all emphasise the importance of storing gas cylinders in a suitable designated area.

Storage of LPG

55   Detailed guidance on storing LPG has been published in the LP Gas Association Code of Practice: *Storage of full and empty LPG cylinders and cartridges*[48]. Guidance for industry on the storage of gas cylinders, LPG and others, may be found in BCGA's publication GN 2[49].

56   The LPGA publications recommend that oxygen cylinders should not be stored within 3 m of an LPG storage area unless separated by a structure of 30 minutes fire-resisting construction. Acetylene cylinders may be stored outdoors with LPG unless the total quantity of LPG exceeds 50 kg, when separation by a minimum of 3 m or a fire wall is recommended. Similarly, cylinders of acetylene may also be kept indoors with LPG in specially designed buildings otherwise dedicated to LPG storage.

Storage of gases other than LPG

Outdoor storage

57   It is recommended that outdoor storage areas for the other fuel gases and oxygen used in welding and cutting follow the principles described in BCGA guidance note GN 2[49].

58   Storage areas should preferably be in clear open air and in a secure compound free, or well separated, from toxic, corrosive or easily ignited combustible materials (eg timber or paper), flammable liquids and general rubbish. Security may be achieved by surrounding the compound with a substantial and robust fence, eg mesh welded panels or chain link fencing. To further aid security, gas cylinders should not be stored within 1 m of the property boundary. Weather protection and a suitable base are advisable to reduce corrosion and prevent overheating by solar radiation.

59   The important precaution of protecting gas cylinders from thermal radiation from nearby fire-risks may be achieved by separating the storage compound from the property boundary and any buildings constructed of combustible materials, or any fixed sources of ignition by an adequate distance or a fire wall. Where a fire wall is used, gas cylinders may be stored next to it. Separation distances need to be determined on the basis of the potential heat output of likely fires. If more than 40 acetylene cylinders are kept in the store, it is advisable to increase the separation distance between the storage area and any building that houses a vulnerable population (eg sleeping people) to give them additional protection from thermal radiation or jet flames. A minimum distance of 8 m is suggested, but this may be influenced by local circumstances or reduced by the presence of a fire wall.

Separate storage building

60   When gas cylinders other than LPG are stored in a separate building, the following design and other features need to be taken into account.

- The building needs to be constructed of substantially non-combustible materials, to avoid a fire threat to the stored cylinders.

- If the building has inadequate separation distances from any site boundary or other building (see paragraph 59), walls on the affected sides need to be built of not less than 30 minutes fire-resisting construction.

- Adequate ventilation should be ensured, ideally by means of natural ventilation openings onto a safe place in the open air. At least five air changes per hour are needed. Normally, this should be achievable with well-dispersed openings totalling 2.5% of the total area of the walls and roof using, for example, air bricks at both high and low levels possibly also with metal mesh doors or gates. The openings need to ensure an adequate cross flow of air that can safely disperse any small leaks from cylinder valves.

- Mechanical ventilation will be necessary if natural ventilation is inadequate for any reason.

- A storage building containing fuel gases needs to have wall sections, or a lightweight roof, which can act as explosion relief to prevent catastrophic failure of the whole building structure following an internal gas explosion. Explosion relief needs to vent to a safe place; it is inappropriate for it to be in walls that need to be of fire-resisting construction.

- There is a need to control sources of ignition by prohibiting smoking and other possible sources. If the building contains fuel gases, it needs to be designated a hazardous area as defined in British Standard BS EN 60079[50] for the purpose of selecting, installing and maintaining any electrical equipment.

- Access to the building should be restricted to prevent unauthorised tampering and vandalism.

Storage areas within a building

61   When gas cylinders other than LPG are kept in a specially designed storage area within a building, the design and other features in paragraph 60 still apply, but it is recommended that the following also be taken into account.

- The internal walls and ceilings surrounding the store need to be substantially constructed (preferably of brick or concrete) and have not less than 30 minutes fire resistance. Substantial construction should ensure that any explosion is preferentially vented to the outside of the building.

- On those relatively rare occasions when the building is also used for residential purposes (eg a flat above a shop in which a small number of cylinders are kept), a suitable and properly maintained automatic fire detection system is strongly recommended, installed in the cylinder storage area and with an audible alarm in the residential accommodation. Note that this recommendation is without prejudice to any requirement to provide an alarm under the Fire Precautions Act 1971[51].

Mixed cylinder storage

62 In a mixed gas store, the procedures described earlier in this section should be followed for each gas involved. In addition, it is good practice to segregate the gases according to the hazards involved, eg flammable, oxidising, toxic and corrosive. Segregation

Figure 8 Storage of cylinders - fixed, upright in a well ventilated area

may be achieved by a distance of at least 3 m or with a 30 minute fire-resisting wall.

Cylinders in use

Cylinders connected for use

63   Cylinders ready for use and connected to equipment may be kept inside a workroom. A spare cylinder of fuel gas and oxygen may also be kept there. Both the connected and the spare cylinders should be securely mounted in wheeled trolleys or safely fixed against a wall or otherwise prevented from falling over. They should be in a well ventilated area within the workroom and well away from any combustible materials.

Keeping fuel gas cylinders upright

64   It is important to keep acetylene cylinders upright immediately before and during use - to stop acetone carrying over when the cylinder valve is opened. LPG cylinders should also be kept upright unless they are specifically designed for use in a horizontal position.

Piped gas supplies

65   The preferred arrangement for piped gas supplies is to supply gas to the points where it is to be used by means of distribution pipework leading into the work area from an external cylinder supply point or manifold installation. The number of gas cylinders stored inside buildings is then kept to a minimum. Storage requirements for the cylinders outside have been covered in paragraphs 57-59.

Cylinder handling

66   If a cylinder is dropped, its valve may be damaged and the gas suddenly released. The result may be a 'rocket-propelled' cylinder, fire and explosion. Care is needed to avoid cylinders falling and from coming into violent contact with other cylinders.

67   Manual handling of heavy gas cylinders easily results in accidents causing back strain, trapped fingers, bruising to hands or

Figure 9 Cylinders on wheeled trolley

feet, etc. The aim should be to avoid the need for anyone having to move gas cylinders by hand. Where this is not reasonably practicable, employers should carry out an assessment of the handling operation in accordance with the requirements of regulation 4(1)(b)(i) of the Manual Handling Operations Regulations 1992[52]. The risks indicated by the assessment should be reduced as far as it is reasonably practicable. Guidance on these Regulations is available in HSE's booklet L23[53]. Moving cylinders on wheeled trolleys designed for the purpose (with the cylinders held securely on the trolley during movement) minimises the risks of injury or of damaged valves. If cylinders are not kept on the trolley during use, it is advisable to ensure they are securely anchored in an upright position, eg fastened with safety chains to strong supports or building walls. Further guidance on the handling of cylinders may be found in BCGA's guidance note GN 3[54].

68   Factors to be considered in the mechanical handling of cylinders include the following:

- wherever possible, appropriate mechanical handling techniques (eg cranes, lifts, cradles, platforms or slings) should be used for loading and unloading delivery vehicles and for other cylinder handling;
- the use of magnets, chains or ropes may be dangerous unless they are properly secured;
- cylinders may be moved by fork-lift truck but they should be fixed securely in a frame or other carrying structure suitable for the purpose;
- cylinders should only be lifted by their valve or valve shroud if the gas supplier has confirmed they are designed for this purpose;

Figure 10 Cylinders on a carrying frame moved by fork-lift truck

●   it is dangerous to use cylinders as rollers or supports, or for any other purpose for which they have not been designed.

PERSONAL PROTECTIVE EQUIPMENT

69   The use of gas welding and cutting equipment brings risk of:

- burns to exposed flesh from the blowpipe flame, the blowpipe nozzle, the workpiece, hot particles, slag or molten metal, or from clothing fires;
- eye injuries from heat, intense light or ultra-violet radiation, or from contact with hot particles, slag, molten metal and sparks;
- injuries to feet, hands and other parts of the body from unexpected movement of heavy objects such as workpieces and gas cylinders.

70   Where these and other personal risks cannot adequately be controlled by means such as engineering controls or safe systems of work, personal protective equipment (PPE) should be provided for the operatives. An assessment should be carried out in accordance with regulation 6 of the Personal Protective Equipment at Work Regulations 1992[55] to determine whether the PPE provided is suitable. These Regulations also include requirements for the maintenance and replacement of PPE. Guidance on the Regulations is given in HSE's booklet L25[56]. The Personal Protective Equipment (EC Directive) Regulations 1992[57] will require almost all PPE supplied for use at work to be certified by an independent inspection body and to meet basic safety requirements. The product can then be marked with the 'CE' mark.

71   Considerations for specific items of PPE include the following.

- Eye protection is invariably necessary, and face and neck protection is often needed too. Equipment is suitable for welding and cutting operations if it meets the requirements of British Standard BS EN 175[58] and BS EN 169[59].
- Hand and arm protection against naked flames and hot surfaces is normally needed. Chromed leather gloves or gauntlets, for example, are fire retardant and suitable for welding applications.
- Flame retardant protective clothing is recommended for the rest of the body where appropriate. It is mainly manufactured from flame retardant cotton or woollen materials. The need for overalls, caps, aprons, sleeves, etc depends on the welding or cutting process in hand. Clothing meeting the requirements of BS EN 470[60] or equivalent is suitable.

● Protection against personal injuries from mechanical and manual handling hazards may be needed, eg when moving and handling cylinders. Safety footwear with steel toe-caps capable of resisting a heavy falling object may be required. Equipment meeting the requirements of BS 4676[61] or equivalent is suitable.

OPERATING PROCEDURES

Training

72 It is a requirement of regulation 9 of the Provision and Use of Work Equipment Regulations 1998[9] that anyone using work equipment receives adequate training in its use for purposes of health and safety. This includes training in the methods that may be adopted when using the work equipment, any risks that this use entails and the precautions to be taken. The requirement extends beyond those using the equipment to include those supervising or managing them.

73 Regulation 13 of the Management of Health and Safety at Work Regulations 1999[1] also requires that employees receive adequate health and safety training. The training needs to take into account the risks associated with the work as identified by the risk assessment which is required by regulation 3. Subjects described elsewhere in this publication which are relevant to the training include:

- hazards associated with the gases used in welding and cutting;
- selection and operation of suitable equipment;
- the role of safety devices;
- fire and emergency procedures;
- correct operating procedures.

74 Training may be required even though an employee holds relevant formal qualifications. Further guidance is given in HSE's Approved Code of Practice L21[62] on the Management of Health and Safety at Work Regulations 1999.

Normal operations

Pre-use equipment check

75 Before starting work, it is important to check that all the correct items of equipment are available for the gases being used, all necessary safety devices are fitted and that the equipment is undamaged. Pressure regulators designated for use with one gas are not interchangeable for use with another. Equipment that appears to have been modified may not be suitable and may be dangerous; it should be examined before use by a knowledgeable person. Damaged or defective hose or hose assemblies should only be replaced or repaired by a competent person.

76   It is advisable to check all connections for leakage using a detergent solution. On equipment with many joints, eg a manifold system, it would be good practice, also, to use a manometer or similar device to indicate any leaks in the system. If there are leaks which cannot easily be stopped, the gas supply should be isolated and the leaking components taken out of service, replaced or repaired. If the leak is at a cylinder valve or pressure regulator ('bull-nose') connection, the cylinder should be removed to a safe place in the open air. If it is a fuel gas cylinder, it should be taken well clear of any source of ignition. Excessive force should never be used on cylinder valve spindles or hexagon nuts of regulator connections in an attempt to stop a leak. Neither are sealing tape nor other jointing materials recommended for use in an attempt to prevent leaks between metal - metal surfaces that are designed to be gas tight. With an oxygen cylinder, this bad practice could result in initiation of a metal-oxygen fire.

77   In cold weather, moisture trapped in the equipment may freeze and, for example, cause valves to malfunction. It is recommended that equipment is thawed out with hot water and cloths, never with naked flames.

Oxygen - freedom from oil and grease

78   To avoid the risk of fires and explosions when oxygen comes into contact with oil and grease, it is important that the equipment used for welding and cutting is not allowed to become contaminated with these materials. Clothing and cleaning materials should also be kept as free as possible from oil and grease, and the only lubricants used should be those known to be suitable for oxygen service. It is also important to completely remove residues of any solvents used to clean equipment before the equipment is exposed to oxygen.

Oxygen - connecting new gas supplies

79   Many accidents have occurred when a new oxygen supply is first connected to equipment. Some are believed to be a result of the presence of contamination in the cylinder valve or connections. Others have been caused by adiabatic compression of oxygen in the equipment (often the inlet side of the pressure regulator) which produces rapid heating and ignition of internal components. Full

compliance with the test requirements in pressure regulator standards does not entirely eliminate this risk and the following procedure is recommended to minimise both contamination and adiabatic compression hazards:

● wipe the cylinder valve outlet and pressure regulator connection with a clean lint-free cloth;
● ensure by careful examination that both surfaces are clean and free from grease, grit and dirt;
● before fitting the pressure regulator, slowly open the cylinder valve, then quickly close it again (a procedure known as 'snifting') - to dislodge any contamination from within the cylinder valve (Note: cylinders of hydrogen should never be snifted due to the risk of spontaneous ignition of the gas);
● make the equipment connections;
● very slowly open the cylinder valve with the pressure regulator outlet in the closed position;
● slowly open the pressure regulator outlet.

Lighting-up and shutting-down procedures

80   Procedures for lighting up and shutting down welding and cutting blowpipes are listed in Table 1. The sequence is appropriate for oxy-fuel gas equipment and, with very little modification, for air-aspirated blowpipes. If in doubt about the procedure, always follow the manufacturer's recommendations. The full shutting-down procedure is recommended when work is finished for the day or at the end of a shift. Store hoses and blowpipe in a safe place where they are unlikely to be damaged when not in use.

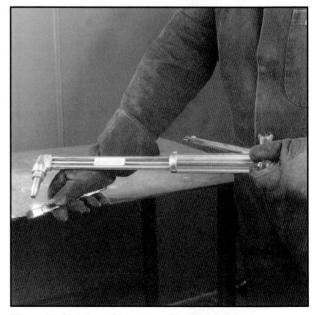

Figure 11 Lighting a blowpipe with a spark lighter

Table 1   Recommended lighting-up/shutting-down procedures

These procedures are appropriate for oxy-fuel gas equipment and, with little modification, also for air-aspirated blowpipes.

Lighting up

1 Ensure that the pre-use equipment checks have been made - see paragraphs 75 and 76.
2 Check that the outlets of adjustable pressure regulators are closed, ie that the pressure-adjusting screw of the regulator is in the fully unwound (anticlockwise) position.
3 Check that the blowpipe valves are closed.
4 Slowly open the cylinder valves (or gas supply point isolation valves) - to avoid sudden pressurisation of any equipment.
5 Adjust pressure regulators to the correct outlet pressures. Or, check that the pressures in distribution pipework are suitable for the equipment and process.
6 Open the oxygen valve at the blowpipe and allow the flow of oxygen to purge* air out of oxygen hose and equipment. If necessary, reset the pressure regulator to ensure correct working oxygen pressure.
7 Close the oxygen valve at the blowpipe.
8 Open the fuel gas valve at the blowpipe and allow the gas flow to purge* air or oxygen from the fuel gas hose and equipment. If necessary, reset the pressure regulator to ensure correct working fuel gas pressure.
9 Light the fuel gas immediately, and preferably with a spark lighter.
10 Open the oxygen valve at the blowpipe and adjust it and the fuel gas valve to give the correct flame setting.

* Purging is important. It removes flammable gas mixtures from the hoses and equipment which could result in explosions and fires when the blowpipe is first lit. It should be carried out in a well ventilated area, and it may take from several seconds to a minute or more depending on the length of hose and gas flow rates

Shutting down

1 Close the fuel gas valve at the blowpipe.
2 Immediately close the oxygen valve at the blowpipe.
3* Close the cylinder valves or gas supply point isolation valves for both oxygen and fuel gas.
4 Close the outlets of adjustable pressure regulators by winding out the pressure-adjusting screws.
5 Open both blowpipe valves to vent the pressure in the equipment.
6 Close the blowpipe valves.

* Step 3 is not necessary when the equipment is to be used again in the immediate future

Handling lit blowpipes

81   Any lit blowpipe is dangerous. It may cause severe burn injury from even the briefest contact with exposed skin, and can easily ignite clothing and other materials. It should be handled with great care. Avoid distractions from the work in hand that may lead to inadvertent contact with the flame. It is advisable to extinguish the flame when work stops temporarily. It is dangerous to hang a lit blowpipe on a gas cylinder shroud or other parts of equipment, or to leave it unattended even for a short period of time.

Emergency procedures

Evacuation

82   Regulation 8 of the Management of Health and Safety at Work Regulations 1999[1] requires employers to establish procedures to be followed by any worker if a situation arises that presents serious and imminent danger. The aim is to set out clear guidance explaining when employees and others at work should stop work and how they should move to a place of safety. Some circumstances may require full evacuation of the workplace; others may be limited to some or all of the workforce moving to a safer part of the workplace. Guidance on application of these Regulations has been published in HSE's Approved Code of Practice L21[62].

Backfires and flashbacks

83   If there is a sustained backfire in a blowpipe (ie the flame returns into the blowpipe and continues burning in the neck or mixing chamber) the recommended first action is to close the oxygen valve on the blowpipe - to prevent internal burning - followed immediately by shutting off the fuel gas at the blowpipe valve. Items 3-6 of the shutting-down procedure of Table 1 may then be followed. When the cause of the backfire has been discovered, the fault rectified and the blowpipe cooled down, the blowpipe may be re-lit.

84   After an unsustained backfire, the recommended procedure is to close the blowpipe control valves, fuel gas first, and follow items 5-10 of the lighting-up procedure in Table 1. If the backfire repeats

itself, the full shutting-down procedure followed by fault
identification and rectification is recommended.

85   If there is a flashback into the hose and equipment, or a hose
fire or explosion, or a fire at the regulator connections or gas
supply outlet points, the first action should be to isolate the oxygen
and fuel gas supplies at the cylinder valves or gas supply outlet
points - but only if this can be done safely. Attempts should only be
made to control a fire using first-aid fire-fighting equipment if there
is no undue risk of personal injury. The emergency fire services
should be called if the fire cannot be put out at once. With the fire
extinguished, the equipment cooled down and no further danger of
re-ignition, the equipment can be examined and defective
components replaced before re-starting the work.

Acetylene cylinders involved in fires

86   There is always a risk of cylinder explosion in any fire
involving an acetylene cylinder, and this risk should be taken into
account in the established emergency procedures (see paragraph
82). Action to deal with acetylene cylinders involved in fires is
always best left to the emergency fire services. Some initial
response may be appropriate, however:

● cool the cylinder by spraying it with water, but only if it is safe
   to do so;
● always call the emergency fire services, even if it is possible
   to close the cylinder valve to control the fire;
● give full consideration to evacuating the whole building and
   not just the immediate work area (and only re-enter when the
   emergency fire services have declared it safe to do so);
● do not attempt to move an acetylene cylinder that has been
   involved in a fire, or to move one which has been affected by
   heat from a nearby fire even if it appears to be cold. It is
   difficult to detect acetylene decomposition which may have
   started inside a cylinder, but it could lead to the cylinder
   exploding if it is not quenched by prolonged cooling.

87   The emergency fire services will advise on any further action
to be taken after the incident has been dealt with.

Work in confined spaces

88 Common situations in which gas welding and cutting might be used in confined spaces include shipbuilding, metal fabrication (eg work on oil rigs, vehicles, boilers, tanks and process plant) and civil engineering construction (eg in tunnel workings). General guidance on entry into confined spaces may be found in HSE's guidance note L101[63].

89 Using compressed gases in confined spaces brings additional risks to those encountered in well-ventilated workrooms or in the open air. Important differences are:

- the means of access and egress are limited;
- the risk of asphyxiation is greater;
- the consequences of a fire or explosion are potentially more severe;
- the likelihood of an accumulation of gases from leaks is greater;
- hazards from welding fumes may be significant in confined spaces (but lie outside the scope of this publication - see paragraph 3).

90 Safety in tunnelling is covered generally by British Standard BS 6164[64], and it is recommended that its precautions for gas welding and cutting are followed in tunnelling work. In other confined spaces, the following are advised:

- a permit-to-work system is adopted - some specialised guidance on this subject has been published by HSE in *Guidance on permit-to-work systems. A guide for the petroleum, chemical and allied industries* HSG250[65], and some aspects of it are applicable to gas welding and cutting in confined spaces more generally;
- a system of fresh air ventilation and fume extraction is provided;
- atmospheric monitoring is used which is capable of detecting any leaks of flammable gas and oxygen enrichment;
- flame arresters incorporating cut-off valves are fitted to all fuel gas and oxygen outlets (see paragraph 48);
- wherever practicable, gas cylinders are not taken into the confined space - if it is necessary, their number and size

should be kept to a minimum and they should be removed when work stops other than for short intervals;

● gas supply hoses and pipework also are removed from any confined space when work is stopped other than for short intervals.

Dangerous operations

Misuse of oxygen

91   Many serious and some fatal accidents have occurred in industry from misuse of oxygen supplies. Guidance on this topic is given in HSE's leaflet No 8 (rev)[66]. Oxygen should never be used to:

● sweeten the air of any workroom or space;
● ventilate a confined space instead of fresh air;
● provide a source of pressure or provide a substitute for compressed air (eg to clear blockages in pipelines or to power air-driven tools);
● blow-down clothing, equipment or work areas to remove dust, etc.

Gas decanting

92   There is a temptation to recharge gas cylinders by connecting them to other cylinders or a gas supply (decanting) when their supply pressure drops below a useful level. The Carriage of Dangerous Goods (Classification, Packaging and Labelling) and Use of Transportable Gas Receptacles Regulations 1996[14] applies to the filling of gas containers, and gas decanting should not be carried out unless the requirements of these Regulations are met.

FIRE PRECAUTIONS

Fire prevention

93   The fire hazard from the use of oxy-fuel or air-aspirated blowpipes needs to be assessed before work starts. Fires may arise not only from direct contact of a flame on combustible materials, but also from slag or hot workpieces which may take a considerable time to cool down. The following precautions are advisable:

- move the workpiece to a safe location for the hot work process to be carried out;
- remove any combustible materials (eg flammable liquids, wood, paper, textiles, packaging or plastics) from the vicinity of the work;
- protect any combustible materials that cannot be moved, from close contact with flame, heat, sparks or hot slag - use suitable guards (eg metal sheeting, mineral-fibre boards or blankets);
- check there is no risk of ignition of combustible materials behind guards, walls or partitions where prolonged welding or cutting is to take place;
- use guards to prevent hot particles passing through openings in floors and walls (doorways, windows, etc).

Fire protection

94   It is a sensible precaution to provide suitable and properly maintained first-aid fire-fighting equipment in the vicinity whenever gas welding and cutting is in progress. Advice on what is suitable in specific circumstances may be obtained from the authority with responsibility for enforcing the fire precaution requirements at the workplace (see the Appendix) and from extinguisher suppliers. It may include:

- portable fire extinguishing equipment, eg water or dry-powder fire extinguishers meeting the requirements of British Standard BS EN 3[67] or BS 5423[68], or hose reels complying with BS 5306 Part 1[69] - where there is a risk of fires involving wood, paper, textiles and similar materials;
- dry-powder, foam or CO_2 extinguishers - where the risk of fire involves flammable liquids;
- buckets of dry sand or fire extinguishers containing specially formulated powders - where there is a risk of metal fires.

Figure 12 Flame cutting - use of protective equipment

95   Additional precautions may be necessary when there is an enhanced risk of fire from combustible materials that cannot be moved. It may be appropriate to appoint 'fire watchers' to detect and extinguish incipient fires and sound the alarm if necessary. They will be needed during operations and for a sufficient period afterwards. It may also be appropriate to use buckets of water to damp down and cool the area surrounding a workpiece.

MAINTENANCE, EXAMINATION AND TESTING OF EQUIPMENT

Gas cylinders

90   The Carriage of Dangerous Goods (Classification, Packaging and Labelling) and Use of Transportable Gas Receptacles Regulations 1996[14] places a duty on the owner of any transportable gas cylinder to ensure that it is examined at appropriate intervals for the purposes of determining whether it is safe. Examinations are normally carried out by the gas suppliers (who are usually the owners of the cylinder) in accordance with BS EN 1968[70], BS EN 1800[71] and ISO 10462[72].

Other equipment

97   Effective maintenance of gas welding and cutting equipment is essential to ensure safety, and is required under Section 2 of the Health and Safety at Work etc Act 1974[73] and regulation 6 of the Provision and Use of Work Equipment Regulations 1998[9]. In addition to the pre-use checks described in paragraphs 75 and 76, it is recommended that all the equipment is regularly examined for the following possible defects:

- leaks at any connection (leak testing is also advisable on any occasion when connections are made, when gas leaks are suspected by smell or hissing sound, and after flashbacks or other incidents) - on no account should a flame be used to test for leaks;
- cuts, cracking and abrasion damage to hoses;
- maloperation of non-return valves (ie reverse flow not shutting off);
- internal leakage in pressure regulators (possibly resulting in rising pressure in the outlet side when the outlet valve is set closed);
- damage to the 'bull nose' connections of pressure regulators;
- incorrect operation of pressure gauges;
- build-up of deposits of combustion products in flame arresters (resulting in low gas flow rates);
- damage to or malfunction of any other components in the system.

98   The necessary frequency of the examinations depends on the frequency of use of the equipment and the conditions in which it is used. The aggressive nature of the working environment needs to be taken into account. Any defective equipment should be replaced or repaired by a competent person using parts which are known to be suitable. The use of unsuitable parts could lead to failure and fire or explosion. If there is any doubt, seek advice from the manufacturers of the equipment.

99 Additional guidance on equipment maintenance and replacement/refurbishment intervals can be found in BCGA's Code of Practice CP 7[45].

100 Regulation 8 of the Pressure Systems Safety Regulations 2000[17] requires that 'pipework' as defined in regulation 2 of the same Regulations shall not be operated unless there is in existence a written scheme for examination by a competent person. The equipment used for gas welding, flame cutting and allied processes which is attached to transportable gas cylinders generally includes hoses, hose connections, pressure regulators, safety devices, welding flux dispensers, and blowpipes (torches), and these are covered by the definition of 'pipework'. However, when applied to portable oxy-fuel gas welding and cutting equipment, these Regulations are not considered to require any additional action over and above those discussed in paragraph 97, and a written scheme of examination is not required for this equipment.

APPENDIX
ACETYLENE

Acetylene

Acetylene is covered by the Explosives Act 1975[6]. Although not an explosive as defined by the Act it was made subject to the Act by Order in Council No 30[6] (dated 1937) which deems acetylene to be an explosive for the purposes of the Act because it is unstable and under certain conditions can decompose violently. However, an Order of the Secretary of State (No 9 of 1919)[6] deems acetylene not to be an explosive when contained in a porous mass, subject to certain conditions.

There are other orders and certificates of exemption, made under the Explosives Act but the above are the main ones.

The result is the manufacture of acetylene, a specialised business currently taking place in only three places in the UK, is subject to licensing under the Explosives Act but acetylene in cylinders does not need to be licensed.

The Explosives Act is to be replaced by new regulations but, as acetylene is not an explosive as defined, it will not be subject to the new regime. New regulations will be required for acetylene but until such time as the new regulations can be introduced, acetylene will continue to be subject to the Explosives Act, which will remain in force for this purpose.

APPENDIX ACETYLENE

58

REFERENCES

HSE publications are available from HSE Books, PO Box 1999, Sudbury, Suffolk CO10 2WA Tel: 01787 881165 Fax: 01787 313995 Website: www.hsebooks.co.uk.

British Standards can be obtained in PDF or hard copy formats from the BSI online shop: www.bsigroup.com/Shop or by contacting BSI Customer Services for hard copies only Tel: 020 8996 9001 e-mail: cservices@bsigroup.com.

BCGA publications are available from the British Compressed Gases Association, 1 Gleneagles House, Vernongate, Derby, DE1 1UP, Tel: 01332 225120 Fax: 01332 225101 Website: www.bcga.co.uk.

The Stationery Office publications are available from The Stationery Office, PO Box 29, Norwich NR3 1GN Tel: 0870 600 5522 Fax: 0870 600 5533 e-mail: customer.services@tso.co.uk Website: www.tso.co.uk (They are also available from bookshops.) Statutory Instruments can be viewed free of charge at www.opsi.gov.uk.

ASTM publications are available from the American Society for Testing and Materials, 100 Barr Harbor Drive, West Conshohocken, Pennsylvania, USA Tel: (610) 832-9500 Fax: (610) 832-9555 Website: www.astm.org.

UKLPG and LPGA publications are available from the UKLPG website: www.uklpg.org.

1   *Management of Health and Safety at Work Regulations 1999* SI 1999/3242 The Stationery Office 1999 ISBN 978 0 11 085625 4

2   *Hot work: Welding and cutting on plant containing flammable materials* HSG5 HSE Books 1979 ISBN 0 11 883229 8 **(out of print)**

3   *Assessment of exposure to fume from welding and allied processes* EH 54 HSE Books 1990 ISBN 0 7176 05701 **(out of print)**

4   *The control of exposure to fume from welding, brazing and similar processes* EH 55 HSE Books 1990 ISBN 0 7176 0574 4 **(out of print)**

5   *Take care with acetylene* Leaflet INDG327 HSE Books 2000 (single copy free or priced packs of 10 ISBN 978 0 7176 1817 0) www.hse.gov.uk/pubns/indg327.pdf

6   *Prohibiting the Manufacture, Importation, Keeping, Conveyance or Sale of Acetylene when an Explosive as Defined by the order Order No 30* SR & O 1937/54 HMSO 1937
   The Compressed Acetylene Order SR & O 1947/805 HMSO 1947
   The Explosives Act 1875 Ch 17 HMSO 1875
   Compressed Acetylene in a Porous Substance Order No 9 SR & O 1919/809 HMSO 1919

7   HSE Exemption Certificate No 2 of 1989 issued by the HSE Explosives Inspectorate

8   British Compressed Gases Association Code of Practice CP6 *The safe distribution of acetylene in the pressure range 0 –15 bar (0-22lbf/in²)* Revision 1 1998 BCGA

9   *Provision and Use of Work Equipment Regulations 1998* SI 1998/2306 The Stationery Office 1998 ISBN 978 0 11 079599 7

10   British Standards Institution BS EN 29539: 1992 *Specification for materials for equipment used in gas welding, cutting and allied processes*

11   British Standards Institution BS EN 29090: 1992 *Specification for gas tightness of equipment for gas welding and allied processes*

12   British Standards Institution BS 4N 100-2: 1999 *Aircraft oxygen systems and equipment. Tests for the compatibility of materials in the presence of oxygen* BS 4N 100-6: 1999 *Aircraft oxygen systems and equipment. Guidance and recommendations on the selection of materials for use with oxygen*

13   American Society for Testing and Materials *Standard guide for evaluating metals for oxygen service* ASTM G 94-92 (1998) American Society for Testing and Materials *Standard guide for evaluating non-metallic materials for oxygen service* ASTM G 63-99 (2001)

14   *Carriage of Dangerous Goods (Classification, Packaging and Labelling) and Use of Transportable Gas Receptacles Regulations 1996 (as amended)* SI 1996/2092 The Stationery Office 1996 ISBN 978 0 11 062923 0

15   A list of cylinder standards approved by HSE is given on the HSE website: www.hse.gov.uk. Search for transportable pressure vessels.

16   *The safe use of gas cylinders* INDG308(rev1) HSE Books 2002 (**out of print**)

17   *Pressure Systems Safety Regulations 2000* SI 2000/128 The Stationery Office 2000 ISBN 978 0 11 085836 4

18   British Compressed Gases Association *Industrial gas cylinder manifolds and distribution pipework/pipelines excluding acetylene* Code of Practice CP4 Revision 2: 1998

19   British Compressed Gases Association *The design and construction of manifolds using acetylene gas to a maximum working pressure of 25 bar (362 lbf/in^2)* Code of Practice CP 5 Revision 1: 1998

20   British Compressed Gases Association *Bulk liquid oxygen storage at users' premises* Code of Practice BCGA Revision 2: 1996 CP 19 ISSN 0260-4809

21   *Odorisation of bulk oxygen supplies in shipyards* CS 7 HSE Books 1983 ISBN 0 11 883578 5 (**discontinued, no longer available from HSE Books**)

22   LPGA Code of Practice *Bulk LPG storage at fixed installations. Part 1: Design, installation and operation of vessels located above ground*
Use of LPG in small bulk tanks CHIS4 HSE Books 1999

23   British Standards Institution BS EN 585: 1995 *Gas welding equipment: Pressure regulators for gas cylinders used in welding, cutting and allied processes up to 200 bar*

24 International Standards Organisation BS EN ISO 2503: 1998 *Gas welding equipment. Pressure regulators for gas cylinders used in welding, cutting and allied processes*

25 British Standards Institution BS 3016: 1989 *Specification for pressure regulators and automatic changeover devices for liquefied petroleum gases*

26 International Standards Organisation BS EN ISO 7291: 2001 *Gas welding equipment. Pressure regulators for manifold systems used in welding, cutting and allied processes up to 300 bar*

27 British Standards Institution BS EN 562: 1995 *Gas welding equipment. Pressure gauges used in welding, cutting and allied processes*

28 International Standards Organisation ISO 5171: 1980 *Pressure gauges used in welding, cutting and related processes*

29 British Standards Institution BS EN 837-1: 1998 *Pressure gauges. Bourdon tube pressure gauges. Dimensions, metrology, requirements and testing*

30 British Standards Institution BS EN 559: 1994 *Gas welding equipment: Rubber hoses for welding, cutting and allied processes*

31 International Standards Organisation ISO 3821: 1998 *Gas welding equipment. Rubber hoses for welding, cutting and allied processes*

32 British Standards Institution BS 3212: 1991 *Specification for flexible rubber tubing, rubber hose and rubber hose assemblies for use in LPG vapour phase and LPG/air installations*

33 British Standards Institution BS EN 1327:1996 *Gas welding equipment. Thermoplastic hoses for welding and allied processes*

34 British Standards Institution BS EN 14114 *Gas welding equipment. Acetylene manifold systems for welding and allied processes*

35   British Standards Institution BS EN 560: 1995 *Gas welding equipment. Hose connections for welding, cutting and allied processes*

36   International Standards Organisation ISO 3253: 1998 *Gas welding equipment. Hose connections for welding, cutting and allied processes*

37   British Standards Institution BS EN 561: 1995 *Gas welding equipment: Quck-action couplings with shut-off valves for welding, cutting and allied processes*

38   International Standards Organisation ISO 7289: 1996 *Quick action couplings with shut-off valve for welding, cutting and allied processes*

39   British Standards Institution BS EN 1256: 1996 *Gas welding equipment. Specification for hose assemblies for equipment for welding, cutting and allied processes*

40   British Standards Institution BS EN 5172: 1997 *Manual blowpipes for welding, cutting and heating. Specifications and tests*

41   British Standards Institution BS EN 731: 1998 *Air aspirated hand blowpipes: Specifications and tests*

42   British Standards Institution BS EN 521: 1998 *Specification for dedicated liquefied petroleum gas appliances. Portable vapour pressure liquefied petroleum gas appliances*

43   British Standards Institution BS EN 730: 1995 *Gas welding equipment. Equipment used in gas welding, cutting and allied processes: Safety devices for fuel gases and oxygen or compressed air: General specifications, requirements and tests*

44   International Standards Organisation ISO 5175: 1987 *Equipment used in gas welding, cutting and allied processes: Safety devices for fuel gases and oxygen or compressed air: General specifications, requirements and tests*

45   British Compressed Gases Association *The safe use of oxy-fuel gas equipment (individual portable or mobile cylinder supply)* Code of Practice BCGA CP7 Revision2 1996

46   *The storage of flammable liquids in containers* (Second edition) HSG51 HSE Books 1998 ISBN 978 0 7176 1471 4

47   British Standards Institution BS 6942 *Design and construction of small kits for oxy-fuel gas welding and allied processes*
Part 2: 1989 *Specification for kits using refillable gas containers for oxygen and fuel gas*
British Standards Institution BS EN 1326: 1996 *Gas welding equipment. Small kits for gas brazing and welding*

48   LPGA Code of Practice No 7: *Storage of full and empty LPG cylinders and cartridges*

49   British Compressed Gases Association *Guidance for the storage of gases in transportable cylinders for industrial use* Guidance Note BCGA 1988 GN 2 Revision 2 1997

50   British Standards Institution BS EN 60079-10: 1996, IEC 60079-10: 1995 *Electrical apparatus for explosive gas atmospheres. Electrical installations in hazardous areas (other than mines)*
BS EN 60079-14: 1997, IEC 60079-14: 1996 *Electrical apparatus for explosive gas atmospheres. Electrical installations in hazardous areas (other than mines)*
BS EN 60079-17: 1997, IEC 60079-17: 1996 *Electrical apparatus for explosive gas atmospheres. Inspection and maintenance of electrical installations in hazardous areas (other than mines)*

51   *Fire Precautions Act 1971* Ch 40 The Stationery Office 1971 ISBN 978 0 10 544071 0

52   *Manual Handling Operations Regulations 1992* SI 1992/2793 The Stationery Office 1992 ISBN 978 0 11 025920 8

53   *Manual handling. Manual Handling Operations Regulations 1992 (as amended). Guidance on Regulations* L23 (Third edition) HSE Books 2004 ISBN 978 0 7176 2823 0

54 British Compressed Gases Association *Application of the Manual Handling Operations Regulations to gas cylinders* Guidance Note BCGA 1993 GN 3 ISSN 0260 4809

55 *Personal Protective Equipment at Work Regulations 1992* SI 1992/2966 The Stationery Office 1992 ISBN 978 0 11 025832 4

56 *Personal protective equipment at work (Second edition). Personal Protective Equipment at Work Regulations 1992 (as amended). Guidance on Regulations* L25 (Second edition) HSE Books 2005 ISBN 978 0 7176 6139 8

57 *Personal Protective Equipment (EC Directive) Regulations 1992* SI 1992/3139 The Stationery Office 1992 ISBN 978 0 11 025252 0

58 British Standards Institution BS EN 175: 1997 *Personal protection. Equipment for eye and face protection during welding and allied processes*

59 British Standards Institution BS EN 169: 1992 *Specification for filters for personal eye-protection equipment used in welding and similar operations*

60 British Standards Institution BS 470-1: 1995 *Protective clothing for use in welding and allied processes. General requirements*

61 British Standards Institution BS 4676: 1983 *Specification for gaiters and footwear for protection against burns and impact risks in foundries*

62 *Management of health and safety at work. Management of Health and Safety at Work Regulations 1999. Approved Code of Practice and guidance* L21 (Second edition) HSE Books 2000 ISBN 978 0 7176 2488 1

63 *Safe work in confined spaces. Confined Spaces Regulations 1997. Approved Code of Practice, Regulations and guidance* L101 (Second edition) HSE Books 2009 ISBN 978 0 7176 6233 3

64 British Standards Institution BS 6164: 2001 *Code of practice for safety in tunnelling in the construction industry*

65   *Guidance on permit-to-work systems. A guide for the petroleum, chemical and allied industries* HSG250 HSE Books 2005 ISBN 978 0 7176 2943 5

66   *Take care with oxygen* Leaflet HSE8(rev2) HSE Books 2007 www.hse.gov.uk/pubns/hse8.pdf

67   British Standards Institution BS EN 3-5: 1996 *Portable fire extinguishers. Specification and supplementary test*

68   British Standards Institution BS 5423: 1987 *Specification for portable fire extinguishers*

69   British Standards Institution BS 5306 *Fire extinguishing installations and equipment on premises* Part 1: 1976 *Hydrant systems, hose reels and foam inlets*

70   British Standards Institution BS EN 1968: 2002 *Inspection and testing of seamless steel cylinders*

71   British Standards Institution BS EN 1800: 1999 *Transportable gas cylinders. Acetylene cylinders. Basic requirements and definition*

72   ISO 10462: 1944 *Cylinders for dissolved acetylene - Periodic inspection and maintenance*

73   *Health and Safety at Work etc Act 1974* Ch 37 The Stationery Office 1974 ISBN 978 0 10 543774 1

Further information

HSE priced and free publications are available by mail order from HSE Books, PO Box 1999, Sudbury, Suffolk CO10 2WA Tel: 01787 881165 Fax: 01787 313995 Website: www.hsebooks.co.uk (HSE priced publications are also available from bookshops and free leaflets can be downloaded from HSE's website: www.hse.gov.uk.)

For information about health and safety ring HSE's Infoline Tel: 0845 345 0055 Fax: 0845 408 9566 Textphone: 0845 408 9577 e-mail: hse.infoline@natbrit.com or write to HSE Information Services, Caerphilly Business Park, Caerphilly CF83 3GG.

British Standards can be obtained in PDF or hard copy formats from the BSI online shop: www.bsigroup.com/Shop or by contacting BSI Customer Services for hard copies only Tel: 020 8996 9001 E-mail: cservices@bsigroup.com.

The Stationery Office publications are available from The Stationery Office, PO Box 29, Norwich NR3 1GN Tel: 0870 600 5522 Fax: 0870 600 5533 e-mail: customer.services@tso.co.uk Website: www.tso.co.uk (They are also available from bookshops.) Statutory Instruments can be viewed free of charge at www.opsi.gov.uk.

Printed and published by the Health and Safety Executive

C2   03/09